Elements of Costing

Workbook

Aubrey Penning

Published by Osborne Books Limited
Tel 01905 748071
Email books@osbornebooks.co.uk
Website www.osbornebooks.co.uk

Design by Laura Ingham

Printed by CPI Group (UK) Limited, Croydon, CR0 4YY, on environmentally friendly, acid-free paper from managed forests.

MIX
Paper from responsible sources
FSC® C019777

British Library Cataloguing in Publication Data
A catalogue record for this book is available from the British Library

ISBN 978 1909173 705

Contents

Introduction

Introduction

Qualifications covered

This book has been written specifically to cover the Unit 'Using Accounting Software' which is mandatory for the following qualifications:

- AAT Foundation Certificate in Accounting – Level 2
- AAT Foundation Diploma in Accounting and Business – Level 2
- AAT Foundation Certificate in Accounting at SCQF Level 5

This book contains Chapter Activities which provide extra practice material in addition to the activities included in the Osborne Books Tutorial text, and Practice Assessments to prepare the student for the computer based assessments. The latter are based directly on the structure, style and content of the sample assessment material provided by the AAT at www.aat.org.uk.

Suggested answers to the Chapter Activities and Practice Assessments are set out in this book.

Osborne Study and Revision Materials

The materials featured on the previous page are tailored to the needs of students studying this Unit and revising for the assessment. They include:

- **Tutorials:** paperback books with practice activities
- **Wise Guides:** pocket-sized spiral bound revision cards
- **Student Zone:** access to Osborne Books online resources
- **Osborne Books App:** Osborne Books ebooks for mobiles and tablets

Visit www.osbornebooks.co.uk for details of study and revision resources and access to online material.

Chapter activities

1 The costing system

1.1 The table below lists some of the characteristics of financial accounting and management accounting systems. Indicate two characteristics for each system by putting a tick in the relevant column of the table below.

Characteristic	Financial Accounting	Management Accounting
Records transactions that have already happened		
Provides accounts that comply with legal requirements		
Looks in detail at future costs and income of products and services		
May use estimates where these are the most suitable form of information		

1.2 Hideaway Ltd is a manufacturer of garden sheds.

Classify the following costs into materials, labour or overheads by putting a tick in the relevant column of the table below.

Cost	Materials	Labour	Overheads
Wood used to make sheds			
Insurance of factory			
Wages of employees who cut window glass to size			
Wages of carpenter who assembles shed panels			

1.3   Hideaway Ltd is a manufacturer of garden sheds.

Classify the following costs by nature (direct or indirect) by putting a tick in the relevant column of the table below.

Cost	Direct	Indirect
Wood used to make sheds		
Insurance of factory		
Wages of employees who cut window glass to size		
Wages of carpenter who assembles shed panels		

1.4   Dave's Plaice is a take away fish and chip shop.

Classify the following costs by putting a tick in the relevant column of the table below.

Cost	Direct Materials	Direct Labour	Indirect Costs
Potatoes used to make chips			
Maintenance of cooking equipment			
Wages of employees who fry fish and chips			
Gas to cook fish and chips			

1.5   Trendy Limited manufactures clothing.

Classify the following costs by function (production, administration, or selling and distribution) by putting a tick in the relevant column of the table below.

Cost	Production	Administration	Selling and Distribution
Purchases of cloth			
Salespeople's salaries			
Insurance of office building			
Salaries of sewing machinists			

2 Cost centres and overhead absorption

2.1 Omega Ltd, a manufacturer of furniture, uses a numerical coding structure based on one profit centre and three cost centres as outlined below. Each code has a sub-code so each transaction will be coded as ***/***

Profit/Cost Centre	Code	Sub-classification	Sub-code
Sales	100	UK Sales	100
		Overseas Sales	200
Production	200	Direct Cost	100
		Indirect Cost	200
Administration	300	Indirect Cost	200
Selling and Distribution	400	Indirect Cost	200

Code the following income and expense transactions, which have been extracted from purchase invoices, sales invoices and payroll, using the table below.

Transaction	Code
Factory lighting	
Warehouse repairs	
Sales to Newcastle, UK	
Sales to India	
Materials to upholster chairs	
Factory maintenance wages	

2.2   Smooth Running Limited operates a garage that repairs and maintains cars. It uses a coding system for its costs (materials, labour or overheads) and then further classifies each cost by nature (direct or indirect cost) as below. So, for example, the code for direct materials is A100.

Element of Cost	Code	Nature of Cost	Code
Materials	A	Direct	100
		Indirect	200
Labour	B	Direct	100
		Indirect	200
Overheads	C	Direct	100
		Indirect	200

Code the following costs, extracted from invoices and payroll, using the table below.

Cost	Code
Wages of trainee mechanic	
Wages of receptionist	
Oil used for car servicing	
Depreciation of electronic tuning equipment used for car servicing	
Replacement parts used for car repairs	

2.3 Highstyle Limited is a company that owns two hairdressing salons. One salon is called Bonkers, and the other is called Hats-off. Each salon is an investment centre.

The following is an extract from the coding manual used by the company.

Investment Centre	Code
Bonkers Salon	B
Hats-off Salon	H
Revenue, Cost, or Investment	**Code**
Salon sales revenue	100
Salon purchase of hair products	200
Labour costs	300
Overheads	400
Investment in shop assets	900

Each code consists of a letter followed by a 3 digit number.

Complete the following table with the appropriate codes.

Transaction	Code
Sales in Bonkers Salon	
Purchase of new barber chair for Hats-off Salon	
Purchase of new wall mirrors for Bonkers Salon	
Purchase of hair products for Bonkers Salon	
Cost of rent at Bonkers shop	
Cost of paying wages of Hats-off stylist	

2.4 A company has a single cost centre in its factory where several different products are made. The following budgeted data relates to the factory:

Overheads	£245,000
Total production (all products)	61,250
Direct labour hours	17,500
Machine hours	12,250

Product K is one of the products made in the factory. It has the following data per unit:

Direct materials cost	£16.00
Direct labour cost	£25.00
Direct labour hours	2 hours
Machine hours	1.5 hours

- Complete the following table to show the alternative overhead absorption rates and the total cost per unit of Product K using the each absorption method.

- State which one of the three overhead absorption methods is least likely to be appropriate for this company, and why.

Overhead absorption method	Units of output £	Direct labour hours £	Machine hours £
Overhead absorption rate			
Product K costs:			
Direct materials			
Direct labour			
Overheads			
Total costs			

2.5   A company has a single cost centre in its factory where several different products are made. The following budgeted data relates to the factory:

Overheads	£486,900
Direct labour hours	57,500
Machine hours	35,850

Product M is one of the products made in the factory. It has the following data per unit:

Direct materials cost	£33.80
Direct labour cost at £11.00 per hour	£33.00
Machine hours	2.5 hours

• Complete the following table to show the alternative overhead absorption rates and the total cost per unit of Product M using each absorption method. Round the overhead absorption rate to four decimal places of £, and calculate the overhead absorbed to the nearest penny.

Overhead absorption method	Direct labour hours £	Machine hours £
Overhead absorption rate		
Product M costs:		
Direct materials		
Direct labour		
Overheads		
Total costs		

2.6 Dai Limited is a manufacturing company with two cost centres in its factory; Assembly and Finishing. Both cost centres are labour intensive. The following data relates to the cost centres:

	Assembly	Finishing	Total
Budgeted indirect costs	£101,600	£56,800	£158,400
Budgeted direct labour hours	39,500	22,250	61,750

One of the products made in the factory is Product Z. Its manufacture takes 6 hours direct labour in Assembly, and 2 hours 30 minutes direct labour in Finishing.

Using the following tables, calculate the overhead absorption rates and the overheads that are absorbed into each unit of Product Z. Round all amounts to the nearest penny.

	Budgeted indirect costs £	Budgeted direct labour hours	Overhead absorption rate £
Assembly			
Finishing			

Product Z	Direct labour hours per unit	Overhead absorption rate £	Overhead absorbed £
Assembly			
Finishing			
Total			

3 Cost behaviour

3.1 Falcon Ltd is a manufacturer of toys.

Classify the following costs by their behaviour (fixed, variable, or semi-variable) by putting a tick in the relevant column of the table below.

Cost	Fixed	Variable	Semi-Variable
Managers' salaries			
Production workers paid a fixed wage plus a production-based bonus			
Packaging materials for finished toys			
Factory insurance			

3.2 Complete the table below showing fixed costs, variable costs, total costs and unit cost at the different levels of production. Calculate unit cost to the nearest penny where appropriate.

Units	Fixed Costs	Variable Costs	Total Costs	Unit Cost
1,000	£20,000	£5,000	£25,000	£25.00
2,000	£	£	£	£
3,000	£	£	£	£
4,000	£	£	£	£

3.3 Omega Ltd is costing a single product which has the following cost details:

Variable Costs per unit

Materials   £5

Labour   £4

Total Fixed Overheads   £90,000

Complete the following total cost and unit cost table for a production level of 15,000 units.

	Total Cost	Unit Cost
Materials	£	£
Labour	£	£
Fixed Overheads	£	£
Total	£	£

3.4 A semi-variable cost totals £78,500 when the activity level is 10,000 units and totals £143,500 when the activity level is 20,000 units.

Use the following tables to:

- Calculate the variable costs (per unit) and the fixed costs (in total)

- Calculate the total costs at the activity levels shown

Variable cost calculation	Total costs £	Units
High data		
Low data		
Difference		
Variable Cost per Unit £		

Fixed cost calculation	Number of units	Costs £
Total costs		
Variable costs		
Fixed costs		

Total cost calculation	Variable costs £	Fixed costs £	Total costs £
14,000 units			
16,000 units			
18,000 units			

3.5 A semi-variable cost totals £59,200 when the 4,000 units are made and totals £91,925 when 7,500 units are made.

Use the following tables to:

• Calculate the variable costs (per unit) and the fixed costs (in total)

• Calculate the total costs at the activity levels shown

Variable cost calculation	Total costs £	Units
High data		
Low data		
Difference		
Variable Cost per Unit £		

Fixed cost calculation	Number of units	Costs £
Total costs		
Variable costs		
Fixed costs		

Total cost calculation	Variable costs £	Fixed costs £	Total costs £
5,000 units			
6,000 units			
7,000 units			

3.6 Identify the type of cost behaviour (fixed, variable, or semi-variable) described in each statement by ticking the relevant boxes in the table below.

Statement	Fixed	Variable	Semi-Variable
At 4,000 units the cost is £10,000, and at 7,500 units the cost is £18,750			
At 2,500 units the cost is £20 per unit, and at 12,500 units the cost is £4 per unit			
At 1,200 units the cost is £4,100 and at 4,800 units the cost is £14,900			

4 Inventory valuation and the manufacturing account

4.1 Identify the correct inventory (stock) valuation method from the characteristic given by putting a tick in the relevant column of the table below.

Characteristic	FIFO	LIFO	AVCO
Issues of inventory are valued at the oldest purchase cost			
Issues of inventory are valued at the average of the cost of purchases			
Inventory balance is valued at the most recent purchase cost			

4.2 Identify whether the following statements about inventory (stock) valuation are true or false by putting a tick in the relevant column of the table below.

	True	False
FIFO costs issues of inventory at the average purchase price		
AVCO costs issues of inventory at the oldest purchase price		
LIFO costs issues of inventory at the most recent purchase price		
LIFO values inventory balance at the most recent purchase price		
FIFO values inventory balance at the most recent purchase price		
AVCO values inventory balance at the latest purchase price		

4.3   Omega Ltd has the following movements in a certain type of inventory into and out of its stores for the month of March:

Date	Receipts		Issues	
	Units	**Cost**	**Units**	**Cost**
March 5	300	£900		£
March 8	200	£800		£
March 12	500	£2,200		£
March 18			600	£
March 25	400	£2,000		£

Complete the table below for the issue and closing inventory values.

Method	Value of Issue on 18 March	Inventory at 31 March
FIFO	£	£
LIFO	£	£
AVCO	£	£

4.4 Place the following headings and amounts into the correct format of a manufacturing account on the right side of the table, making sure that the arithmetic of your account is accurate. The first entry has been made for you.

	£		£
Direct cost		Opening inventory of raw materials	10,000
Opening inventory of raw materials	10,000		
Closing inventory of work in progress	19,000		
Direct labour	30,000		
Opening inventory of work in progress	10,000		
Closing inventory of finished goods	14,000		
Closing inventory of raw materials	11,000		
Cost of goods sold			
Raw materials used in manufacture	43,000		
Purchases of raw materials	44,000		
Cost of goods manufactured			
Opening inventory of finished goods	25,000		
Manufacturing overheads	21,000		
Manufacturing cost			

Calculate the following amounts:

- Direct cost
- Manufacturing cost
- Cost of goods manufactured
- Cost of goods sold

4.5   Magnum Ltd has the following movements in a certain type of inventory into and out of its stores for the month of September:

Date	Receipts		Issues	
	Units	**Cost**	**Units**	**Cost**
September 5	400	£800		£
September 8	250	£450		£
September 12			300	£
September 18	500	£1,200		£
September 25	400	£1,000		£

Complete the table below for the issue and closing inventory values.

Calculate final values to nearest £.

Method	Value of Issue on September 12	Inventory at 30 September
FIFO	£	£
LIFO	£	£
AVCO	£	£

5   Labour costs

5.1   Identify the labour payment method by putting a tick in the relevant column of the table below.

Payment Method	Time-rate	Piecework	Time-rate plus bonus
Labour is paid based entirely on the production level achieved			
Labour is paid according to hours worked, plus an extra amount if an agreed level of output is exceeded			
Labour is paid only according to hours worked			

5.2   Greville Ltd pays a time-rate of £12 per hour to its direct labour for a standard 38 hour week. Any of the labour force working in excess of 38 hours is paid an overtime rate of £18 per hour.

Calculate the gross wage for the week for the two workers in the table below.

Worker	Hours Worked	Basic Wage	Overtime	Gross Wage
A Summer	38	£	£	£
S Cambridge	43	£	£	£

5.3   Omega Ltd uses a piecework method to pay labour in one of its factories. The rate used is £1.30 per unit produced.

Calculate the gross wage for the week for the two workers in the table below.

Worker	Units Produced in Week	Gross Wage
V Singh	320	£
A Evans	390	£

5.4   Omega uses a time-rate method with bonus to pay its direct labour in one of its factories. The time-rate used is £10 per hour and a worker is expected to produce 20 units an hour. Anything over this and the worker is paid a bonus of £0.25 per unit.

Calculate the gross wage for the week including bonus for the three workers in the table below.

Worker	Hours Worked	Units Produced	Basic Wage	Bonus	Gross Wage
A Samuel	35	650	£	£	£
J McGovern	35	775	£	£	£
M Schaeffer	35	705	£	£	£

5.5   Identify the following statements as true or false by putting a tick in the relevant column of the table below.

	True	False
Indirect labour costs can be identified with the goods being made or the service being produced		
Direct labour costs never alter when the level of activity changes		
The classification of labour costs into direct and indirect does not depend on the method of calculation of the pay		

6 Providing information – budgets and variances

6.1 Identify the following statements as being true or false by putting a tick in the relevant column of the table below.

	True	False
A budget is a financial plan for an organisation that is prepared in advance		
If actual costs are more than budgeted costs the result is a favourable variance		

6.2 Greville Ltd has produced a performance report detailing budgeted and actual cost for last month.

Calculate the amount of the variance for each cost type and then determine whether it is adverse or favourable by putting a tick in the relevant column of the table below.

Cost Type	Budget £	Actual £	Variance	Adverse	Favourable
Direct Materials	93,500	94,200	£		
Direct Labour	48,700	47,800	£		
Production Overheads	28,000	31,200	£		
Administration Overheads	28,900	27,700	£		
Selling and Distribution Overheads	23,800	23,100	£		

6.3 The following performance report for last month has been produced for Greville Ltd as summarised in the table below. Any variance in excess of 4% of budget is thought to be significant and should be reported to the relevant manager for review and appropriate action.

Examine the variances in the table below and indicate whether they are significant or not significant by putting a tick in the relevant column.

Cost Type	Budget £	Variance	Adverse/ Favourable	Significant	Not Significant
Direct Materials	93,500	£700	A		
Direct Labour	48,700	£900	F		
Production Overheads	28,000	£3,200	A		
Administration Overheads	28,900	£1,200	F		
Selling and Distribution Overheads	23,800	£700	F		

6.4 It was noted from the performance report for Greville Ltd for an earlier month that the following cost variances were significant:

- Direct Materials Cost

- Selling and Distribution Overheads

These variances needed to be reported to the relevant managers for review and appropriate action if required.

Select from the following list a relevant manager for each significant variance to whom the performance report should be sent:

HR Manager

Production Manager

Sales Manager

Training manager

Managing Director

Distribution Manager

Purchasing Manager

Variance	Manager
Direct Materials Cost	
Selling and Distribution Overheads	

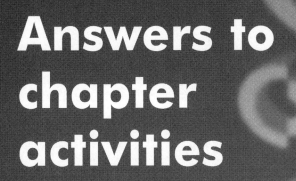

Answers to chapter activities

1 The costing system

1.1

Characteristic	Financial Accounting	Management Accounting
Records transactions that have already happened	✔	
Provides accounts that comply with legal requirements	✔	
Looks in detail at future costs and income of products and services		✔
May use estimates where these are the most suitable form of information		✔

1.2

Cost	Materials	Labour	Overheads
Wood used to make sheds	✔		
Insurance of factory			✔
Wages of employees who cut window glass to size		✔	
Wages of carpenter who assembles shed panels		✔	

1.3

Cost	Direct	Indirect
Wood used to make sheds	✔	
Insurance of factory		✔
Wages of employees who cut window glass to size	✔	
Wages of carpenter who assembles shed panels	✔	

1.4

Cost	Direct Materials	Direct Labour	Indirect Costs
Potatoes used to make chips	✔		
Maintenance of cooking equipment			✔
Wages of employees who fry fish and chips		✔	
Gas to cook fish and chips			✔

1.5

Cost	Production	Administration	Selling and Distribution
Purchases of cloth	✔		
Salespeople's salaries			✔
Insurance of office building		✔	
Salaries of sewing machinists	✔		

2 Cost centres and overhead absorption

2.1

Transaction	Code
Factory lighting	200/200
Warehouse repairs	400/200
Sales to Newcastle, UK	100/100
Sales to India	100/200
Materials to upholster chairs	200/100
Factory maintenance wages	200/200

2.2

Cost	Code
Wages of trainee mechanic	B100
Wages of receptionist	B200
Oil used for car servicing	A100
Depreciation of electronic tuning equipment used for car servicing	C200
Replacement parts used for car repairs	A100

2.3

Transaction	Code
Sales in Bonkers Salon	B100
Purchase of new barber chair for Hats-off Salon	H900
Purchase of new wall mirrors for Bonkers Salon	B900
Purchase of hair products for Bonkers Salon	B200
Cost of rent at Bonkers shop	B400
Cost of paying wages of Hats-off stylist	H300

2.4

Overhead absorption method	Units of output	Direct labour hours	Machine hours
	£	£	£
Overhead Absorption Rate	4.00	14.00	20.00
Product K Costs:			
Direct Materials	16.00	16.00	16.00
Direct Labour	25.00	25.00	25.00
Overheads	4.00	28.00	30.00
Total Costs	45.00	69.00	71.00

- The units of output method of overhead absorption is least likely to be appropriate since the company makes several different products, and under this system they would all be charged the same amount of overhead.

2.5

Overhead absorption method	Direct labour hours	Machine hours
	£	£
Overhead Absorption Rate	8.4678	13.5816
Product M Costs:		
Direct Materials	33.80	33.80
Direct Labour	33.00	33.00
Overheads	25.40	33.95
Total Costs	92.20	100.75

2.6

	Budgeted indirect costs	Budgeted direct labour hours	Overhead absorption rate
	£		£
Assembly	101,600	39,500	2.57
Finishing	56,800	22,250	2.55

Product Z	Direct labour hours per unit	Overhead absorption rate	Overhead absorbed
		£	£
Assembly	6.0	2.57	15.42
Finishing	2.5	2.55	6.38
Total			21.80

3 Cost behaviour

3.1

Cost	Fixed	Variable	Semi-Variable
Managers' salaries	✔		
Production workers paid a fixed wage plus a production-based bonus			✔
Packaging materials for finished toys		✔	
Factory insurance	✔		

3.2

Units	Fixed Costs	Variable Costs	Total Costs	Unit Cost
1,000	£20,000	£5,000	£25,000	£25.00
2,000	£20,000	£10,000	£30,000	£15.00
3,000	£20,000	£15,000	£35,000	£11.67
4,000	£20,000	£20,000	£40,000	£10.00

3.3

	Total Cost	Unit Cost
Materials	£75,000	£5.00
Labour	£60,000	£4.00
Fixed Overheads	£90,000	£6.00
Total	£225,000	£15.00

3.4

Variable cost calculation	Total costs £	Units
High data	143,500	20,000
Low data	78,500	10,000
Difference	65,000	10,000
Variable Cost per Unit £	6.50	

Fixed cost calculation	Number of units	Costs £
Total Costs	20,000	143,500
Variable Costs		130,000
Fixed Costs		13,500

Total cost calculation	Variable costs £	Fixed costs £	Total costs £
14,000 units	91,000	13,500	104,500
16,000 units	104,000	13,500	117,500
18,000 units	117,000	13,500	130,500

3.5

Variable cost calculation	Total costs £	Units
High data	91,925	7,500
Low data	59,200	4,000
Difference	32,725	3,500
Variable Cost per Unit £	9.35	

Fixed cost calculation	Number of units	Costs £
Total Costs	4,000	59,200
Variable Costs		37,400
Fixed Costs		21,800

Total cost calculation	Variable costs £	Fixed costs £	Total costs £
5,000 units	46,750	21,800	68,550
6,000 units	56,100	21,800	77,900
7,000 units	65,450	21,800	87,250

3.6

Statement	Fixed	Variable	Semi-Variable
At 4,000 units the cost is £10,000, and at 7,500 units the cost is £18,750		✔	
At 2,500 units the cost is £20 per unit, and at 12,500 units the cost is £4 per unit	✔		
At 1,200 units the cost is £4,100 and at 4,800 units the cost is £14,900			✔

4 Inventory valuation and the manufacturing account

4.1

Characteristic	FIFO	LIFO	AVCO
Issues of inventory are valued at the oldest purchase cost	✔		
Issues of inventory are valued at the average of the cost of purchases			✔
Inventory balance is valued at the most recent purchase cost	✔		

4.2

	True	False
FIFO costs issues of inventory at the average purchase price		✔
AVCO costs issues of inventory at the oldest purchase price		✔
LIFO costs issues of inventory at the most recent purchase price	✔	
LIFO values inventory balance at the most recent purchase price		✔
FIFO values inventory balance at the most recent purchase price	✔	
AVCO values inventory balance at the latest purchase price		✔

4.3

Method	Value of Issue on 18 March	Inventory at 31 March
FIFO	£2,140	£3,760
LIFO	£2,600	£3,300
AVCO	£2,340	£3,560

4.4

	£		£
Direct cost		Opening inventory of raw materials	10,000
Opening inventory of raw materials	10,000	Purchases of raw materials	44,000
Closing inventory of work in progress	19,000	Closing inventory of raw materials	11,000
Direct labour	30,000	Raw materials used in manufacture	43,000
Opening inventory of work in progress	10,000	Direct labour	30,000
Closing inventory of finished goods	14,000	Direct cost	
Closing inventory of raw materials	11,000	Manufacturing overheads	21,000
Cost of goods sold		Manufacturing cost	
Raw materials used in manufacture	43,000	Opening inventory of work in progress	10,000
Purchases of raw materials	44,000	Closing inventory of work in progress	19,000
Cost of goods manufactured		Cost of goods manufactured	
Opening inventory of finished goods	25,000	Opening inventory of finished goods	25,000
Manufacturing overheads	21,000	Closing inventory of finished goods	14,000
Manufacturing cost		Cost of goods sold	

- Direct cost   £73,000
- Manufacturing cost   £94,000
- Cost of goods manufactured   £85,000
- Cost of goods sold   £96,000

4.5

Method	Value of Issue on September 12	Inventory at 30 September
FIFO	£600	£2,850
LIFO	£550	£2,900
AVCO	£577	£2,873

5   Labour costs

5.1

Payment Method	Time-rate	Piecework	Time-rate plus bonus
Labour is paid based entirely on the production level achieved		✔	
Labour is paid according to hours worked, plus an extra amount if an agreed level of output is exceeded			✔
Labour is paid only according to hours worked	✔		

5.2

Worker	Hours Worked	Basic Wage	Overtime	Gross Wage
A Summer	38	£456	£0	£456
S Cambridge	43	£456	£90	£546

5.3

Worker	Units Produced in Week	Gross Wage
V Singh	320	£416.00
A Evans	390	£507.00

5.4

Worker	Hours Worked	Units Produced	Basic Wage	Bonus	Gross Wage
A Samuel	35	650	£350.00	£0.00	£350.00
J McGovern	35	775	£350.00	£18.75	£368.75
M Schaeffer	35	705	£350.00	£1.25	£351.25

5.5

	True	False
Indirect labour costs can be identified with the goods being made or the service being produced		✔
Direct labour costs never alter when the level of activity changes		✔
The classification of labour costs into direct and indirect does not depend on the method of calculation of the pay	✔	

6 Providing information – budgets and variances

6.1

	True	False
A budget is a financial plan for an organisation that is prepared in advance	✔	
If actual costs are more than budgeted costs the result is a favourable variance		✔

6.2

Cost Type	Budget £	Actual £	Variance	Adverse	Favourable
Direct Materials	93,500	94,200	£700	✔	
Direct Labour	48,700	47,800	£900		✔
Production Overheads	28,000	31,200	£3,200	✔	
Administration Overheads	28,900	27,700	£1,200		✔
Selling and Distribution Overheads	23,800	23,100	£700		✔

6.3

Cost Type	Budget £	Variance	Adverse/ Favourable	Significant	Not Significant
Direct Materials	93,500	£700	A		✔
Direct Labour	48,700	£900	F		✔
Production Overheads	28,000	£3,200	A	✔	
Administration Overheads	28,900	£1,200	F	✔	
Selling and Distribution Overheads	23,800	£700	F		✔

6.4

Variance	Manager
Direct Materials Cost	Production Manager or Purchasing Manager
Selling and Distribution Overheads	Sales Manager or Distribution Manager

Practice assessment 1

Task 1

(a) **(1)** Identify **two** examples of terms used to classify cost **by function** from the following list.

Term	
Materials	
Fixed	
Administration	
Indirect	
Production	

(2) Complete the following sentences by using terms from the options:

(i) Costs that remain unchanged per unit of output are **fixed / variable / semi-variable** costs.

(ii) Costs that remain unchanged in total are **fixed / variable / semi-variable** costs.

(b) The table below lists some of the characteristics of financial accounting and management accounting systems.

Indicate which characteristics relate to each system by putting a tick in the relevant column of the table below.

Characteristic	Financial Accounting	Management Accounting
It is concerned with recording historic costs and revenues		
One of its main purposes is to provide information for annual financial statements		
It is accurate, with no use of estimates		
It looks forward to show what is likely to happen in the future		

(c) Octavia Ltd, a manufacturer of food products, uses an alpha-numeric coding structure based on one profit centre and three cost centres as outlined below. Each code has a sub-code so each transaction will be coded as */***

Profit/Cost Centre	Code	Sub-classification	Sub-code
Sales	A	Restaurant Sales	100
		Supermarket Sales	200
Production	B	Direct Cost	100
		Indirect Cost	200
Administration	C	Direct Cost	100
		Indirect Cost	200
Selling and Distribution	D	Direct Cost	100
		Indirect Cost	200

Code the following revenue and expense transactions, which have been extracted from purchase invoices, sales invoices and payroll, using the table below.

Transaction	Code
Factory lighting	
Repairs to warehouse	
Meat for making burgers	
Sales to 'Kings Restaurant'	
Commission to sales staff	
Stationery for Administration	

Task 2

(a) Identify whether the following statements are true or false by putting a tick in the relevant column of the table below.

Statement	True	False
AVCO costs issues of inventory at the most recent purchase price		
FIFO costs issues of inventory at the oldest relevant purchase price		
LIFO costs issues of inventory at the oldest relevant purchase price		
FIFO values closing inventory at the most recent purchase price		
LIFO values closing inventory at the most recent purchase price		
AVCO values closing inventory at the most recent purchase price		

(b) Identify the labour payment method by putting a tick in the relevant column of the table below.

Payment Method	Time-rate	Piecework	Time-rate plus bonus
Labour is paid based entirely on attendance at the workplace			
Labour is paid a basic rate plus an extra amount if an agreed level of production is exceeded			
Labour is paid entirely according to each individual's output			

(c) Identify **two** uses for a budget from the following list:

Showing historical information	
Monitoring against actual costs	
Planning for the future	
Calculating tax owed	
Calculating individuals' pay	

(d)   Complete the following sentences by using terms from the options:

(1)   An individual shop within a chain of shops that is responsible for capital expenditure would be an example of **a cost / an investment / a profit** centre.

(2)   A part of a business may be considered as a profit centre if it has responsibility for **income and costs / just costs / income, costs and investment**.

Task 3

Octavia Ltd has the following movements in a certain type of inventory (stock) into and out of its stores for the month of August:

Date	Receipts		Issues	
	Units	**Cost**	**Units**	**Cost**
August 12	100	£500		£
August 14	350	£1,820		£
August 17	400	£2,200		£
August 18			700	£
August 26	300	£1,680		£

Complete the table below for the issue and closing inventory values.

Method	Value of Issue on 18 August	Inventory at 31 August
FIFO	£	£
LIFO	£	£
AVCO	£	£

Task 4

(a)   Granville Ltd pays a time-rate of £8 per hour to its direct labour for a standard 37 hour week. Any of the labour force working in excess of 37 hours is paid an overtime rate of £16 per hour.

Calculate the gross wage for the week for the two workers in the table below.

Worker	Hours Worked	Basic Wage	Overtime	Gross Wage
A Smith	37	£	£	£
S Collins	41	£	£	£

(b)   Octavia Ltd uses a time-rate method with bonus to pay its direct labour in one of its factories. The time-rate used is £10 per hour and a worker is expected to produce 7 units an hour. Anything over this and the worker is paid a bonus of £0.50 per unit.

Calculate the gross wage for the week including bonus for the three workers in the table below.

Worker	Hours Worked	Units Produced	Basic Wage	Bonus	Gross Wage
A Weaton	40	250	£	£	£
J Davis	40	295	£	£	£
M Laston	40	280	£	£	£

Task 5

Bromyard Ltd is looking to calculate the unit cost of one of the products it makes. It needs to calculate an overhead absorption rate to apply to each unit. The methods it is considering are:

- Per machine hour
- Per labour hour
- Per unit

Total factory activity is forecast as follows:

Machine hours	35,000
Labour hours	60,000
Units	80,000
Overheads	£450,000

(a) Complete the table below to show the possible overhead absorption rates that Bromyard Ltd could use. The absorption rates should be calculated to two decimal places.

	Machine hour	Labour hour	Unit
Overheads £			
Activity			
Absorption rate £			

The following data relates to the making of one unit of the product:

Material	5 kilos at £6 per kilo
Labour	30 minutes at £18 per hour
Production time	20 minutes machine time

(b) Complete the table below (to two decimal places) to calculate the total unit cost, using the three overhead absorption rates you have calculated in (a).

Cost	Machine hour £	Labour hour £	Unit £
Material			
Labour			
Direct cost			
Overheads			
Total unit cost			

Task 6

(a) Identify the type of cost behaviour (fixed, variable, or semi-variable) described in each statement by ticking the relevant boxes in the table below.

Costs	Fixed	Variable	Semi-variable
At 2,000 units the cost is £6,000, and at 9,000 units the cost is £27,000			
At 1,500 units the cost is £2,500, and at 3,500 units the cost is £4,500			
At 1,200 units the cost is £6,000, and at 2,000 units the cost is £3 per unit			

(b) Complete the table below by inserting all costs for activity levels of 2,000 and 6,500 units.

	2,000 units	3,000 units	5,000 units	6,500 units
Variable cost £				
Fixed cost £				
Total cost £		7,800	11,800	

Task 7

A company has the following cost information for the last period:

	£
Purchases of raw materials	48,000
Direct labour	86,000
Indirect labour	14,000
Manufacturing expenses	50,000

Inventory information at the start and end of the period was as follows:

	£
Opening raw materials inventory	9,000
Closing raw materials inventory	10,000
Opening work in progress	9,000
Closing work in progress	11,000
Opening finished goods inventory	30,000
Closing finished goods inventory	25,000

Enter the correct figures for the following costs:

Direct materials used   £ [   ]

Direct cost   £ [   ]

Manufacturing cost   £ [   ]

Cost of goods manufactured   £ [   ]

Cost of sales   £ [   ]

Task 8

A company uses weighted average cost (AVCO) to value the issues of raw materials to production. The following record shows the raw material movements for the raw material for product Z15 in November.

(a) Complete the inventory record. Costs per kilogram (kg) should be completed in £ to three decimal places.

Date	Receipts Qty (kg)	Cost per kg	Total cost £	Issues Qty (kg)	Cost per kg	Total cost £	Balance Qty (kg)	Total cost £
1 Nov							10,000	50,000
6 Nov	15,000	5.20	78,000					
9 Nov				20,000				

(b) Complete the following table to show:

- The costs for the actual November production of 10,000 units of Z15, using the issues of raw materials calculated in part (a)

- The costs that would apply if the November production had been only 8,000 units of Z15

Z15 Units made and sold	10,000	8,000
	£	£
Variable costs:		
Direct materials		
Direct labour	50,000	
Fixed costs:		
Manufacturing overheads	25,000	
Total cost		
Cost per unit (to three decimal places)		

Task 9

(a) The manager of Perform Limited requires a performance report detailing budgeted data, actual data, and variances for last month.

Budgeted data for the month included:

Sales	6,300 units at £45 per unit
Material	3,250 kilos at £15 per kilo
Labour	3,350 hours at £22 per hour
Overheads	£99,500

In the table below, insert the budget amount for each item, calculate each variance, and then determine whether it is adverse or favourable.

Item	Budget £	Actual £	Variance £	Adverse / Favourable
Sales		284,000		
Material		49,560		
Labour		71,600		
Overheads		95,900		

(b) A number of statements about budgeting are set out in the table below.

Identify whether the following statements are true or false.

	True	False
If budgeted sales are 8,000 units at £2.50 per unit, and actual sales value is £22,000, the sales variance is favourable		
If budgeted material costs are 2,000 units at £11.50 per unit, and actual material costs are £22,000, the material cost variance is favourable		
When variances are shown as percentages, the percentage is calculated based on the actual figures		
The total value of all favourable variances can never exceed the total value of all adverse variances		

Task 10

(a)   The managers of Lovejoy Ltd require the budget report below for last month to be completed. In particular they want production cost variances expressed as percentages of budget.

Actual costs were:

Direct materials	£68,950
Direct labour	£89,560
Production overheads	£44,600

Calculate the production cost variances and the variances as a percentage of budget, rounded to two decimal places.

Cost	Budget £	Variance £	Variance %
Direct materials	71,350		
Direct labour	88,500		
Production overheads	44,050		

Mantra Ltd has a policy of identifying variances that exceed 3% of budget as significant, and then reporting only these variances to the appropriate manager(s).

(b)   **(1)**   Examine the variances in the following table and determine whether they are significant or not.

Cost	Budget £	Variance £	Significant
Direct materials	96,350	4,050	
Direct labour	109,500	3,160	
Production overheads	77,055	2,030	

(2)   Identify whether the following statements are true or false:

Statement	True	False
The direct material variance should be reported to the Purchasing Manager and Production Manager		
The direct labour variance should be reported to the Managing Director		
The production overhead variance should be reported to the Training Manager		
The production overhead variance should be reported to the Production Manager		

Practice assessment 2

Task 1

(a) **(1)** Identify **two** examples of terms used to classify cost **by element** from the following list:

Term	
Materials	
Fixed	
Administration	
Indirect	
Labour	

(2) Complete the following sentences by using terms from the options:

(i) Cost of renting factory premises would behave as a **fixed / variable / semi-variable** cost.

(ii) Cost of paying production workers on a piecework basis would behave as a **fixed / variable / semi-variable** cost.

(b) Indicate the characteristics of financial accounting and management accounting by putting a tick in the relevant column of the table below.

Characteristic	Financial Accounting	Management Accounting
The system is subject to many external regulations		
The accounts must be produced in a format that is imposed on the organisation		
The system is governed primarily by its usefulness to its internal users		
The information produced can be in any format that the organisation wishes to use		

(c) Spread Ltd manages projects in the UK and abroad. It uses an alpha numerical coding structure as outlined below. Each code has a sub-code, so each transaction will have a code format AB123.

Activity	Code	Sub-classification	Sub-code
Investment in projects	IP	UK projects	100
		Overseas projects	200
Project revenues	PR	UK projects	100
		Overseas projects	200
Project costs	PC	Material	030
		Labour	040
		Overheads	050

Code the following transactions by entering the appropriate code in the table.

Transaction	Code
Revenue from project in Saudi Arabia	
Cost of material used for project in Saudi Arabia	
Cost of hiring local labour for project in Saudi Arabia	
Investment in project in Saudi Arabia	
Revenue from UK project	
Cost of renting project offices	

Task 2

(a) Identify whether the following statements are true or false by putting a tick in the relevant column of the table below.

Statement	True	False
AVCO uses a weighted average to value both issues and balances		
FIFO will value issues at the most recent prices		
LIFO will value issues at the most recent prices		

(b) An employee is paid £9 per hour and is expected to produce 7 units an hour. Any production in excess of this is paid a bonus of £2.50 per unit.

Identify whether each of the statements below is true or false by putting a tick in the relevant column.

Statement	True	False
If during a 40 hour week the employee produces 300 units a bonus of £50 will apply		
If during a 37 hour week the employee produces 250 units no bonus will apply		
If during a 39 hour week the employee produces 320 units a bonus of £67.50 will apply		

(c) Identify two of the following that are not uses for a budget:

Showing historical information	
Monitoring against actual costs	
Planning for the future	
Coordinating planning activities	
Recording petty cash	

(d) Complete the following sentences by using terms from the options:

(1) Where an organisation produces many different products with different values it **should / should not** use a per unit overhead absorption method.

(2) For a labour-intensive manufacturing organisation, the most appropriate overhead absorption method would be **direct labour hours / machine hours**.

Task 3

A business has the following movements in a certain type of inventory into and out of its stores for the month of February:

Date	Receipts		Issues	
	Units	**Cost**	**Units**	**Cost**
February 5	100	£400		£
February 9	300	£1,260		£
February 13	600	£2,640		£
February 18			800	£
February 26	500	£2,150		£

Complete the table below for the issue costs and closing inventory values.

Method	Cost of Issue on 18 February	Value of Inventory at 28 February
FIFO	£	£
LIFO	£	£
AVCO	£	£

Task 4

All production workers in a factory are paid at a basic rate of £10 per hour. Those who work the evening shift are paid an unsocial hours premium of 10% of basic pay. They are also paid for any overtime at a rate of basic rate plus 25%, but overtime does not also attract an unsocial hour premium. There were ten production workers on the evening shift last month.

The factory sets a target for output each month of 50,000 units for the evening shift. Where this is exceeded, a bonus of £800 is shared between the production workers for every additional 1,000 units. The actual evening shift output last month was 52,000 units.

Complete the following table to show the total labour costs for the evening shift last month.

	Hours	Cost £
Basic hours and pay	1,400	14,000
Unsocial hours premium	1,400	1,400
Overtime hours basic rate	200	2,000
Overtime hours premium	200	500
Bonus payment		1,600
Total pay		19,500

Task 5

Ledbury Ltd is looking to calculate the unit cost of one of the products it makes. It needs to calculate an overhead absorption rate to apply to each unit. The methods it is considering are:

- Per machine hour
- Per labour hour
- Per unit

Total factory activity is forecast as follows:

Machine hours	20,000
Labour hours	35,000
Units	75,000
Overheads	£380,000

(a) Complete the table below to show the possible overhead absorption rates that Ledbury Ltd could use. The absorption rates should be calculated to two decimal places.

	Machine hour	Labour hour	Unit
Overheads £			
Activity			
Absorption rate £			

The following data relates to the making of one unit of the product:

Material	4 kilos at £7.50 per kilo
Labour	15 minutes at £16 per hour
Production time	10 minutes machine time

(b) Complete the table below (to two decimal places) to calculate the total unit cost, using the three overhead absorption rates you have calculated in (a).

Cost	Machine hour £	Labour hour £	Unit £
Material			
Labour			
Direct cost			
Overheads			
Total unit cost			

Task 6

(a)   Identify the type of cost behaviour (fixed, variable, or semi-variable) described in each statement by ticking the relevant boxes in the table below.

Costs	Fixed	Variable	Semi-variable
At 3,000 units the cost is £16,000, and at 6,000 units the cost is £27,000			
At 2,500 units the cost is £7,500, and at 7,500 units the cost is £22,500			
At 1,800 units the cost is £5 per unit, and at 2,000 units the cost is £4.50 per unit			

(b)   Complete the table below by inserting all costs for activity levels of 5,000 and 10,500 units.

	5,000 units	6,000 units	10,000 units	10,500 units
Variable cost £				
Fixed cost £				
Total cost £		22,500	36,500	

Task 7

A company has the following cost information for the last period:

	£
Purchases of raw materials	123,000
Direct labour	156,000
Manufacturing overheads	146,000

Inventory information at the start and end of the period was as follows:

	£
Opening raw materials inventory	13,000
Closing raw materials inventory	27,000
Opening work in progress	27,000
Closing work in progress	39,000
Opening finished goods inventory	35,000
Closing finished goods inventory	33,000

Enter the correct figures for the following costs:

Direct materials used   £

Direct cost   £

Manufacturing cost   £

Cost of goods manufactured   £

Cost of goods sold   £

Task 8

All production workers in a factory are paid at a basic rate of £15 per hour. Where there are no production workers absent at any time during the month, all employees are paid a 2% attendance premium of basic pay.

All production workers are also paid a bonus based on output. The bonus is 50p per employee per month for each average unit per employee that is produced.

During the last month each of the 25 production workers worked 150 hours. There were no absences. The total factory production was 1,000 units for the month.

(a) Complete the following table to show the labour costs per production worker and in total for the month.

	Cost per Production Worker £	Total Cost £
Basic pay		
Attendance premium		
Bonus payment		
Total pay		

(b) Complete the following table to show:

- The costs for the actual month's production of 1,000 units, using the total direct labour cost calculated in part (a)

- The costs that would apply if the month's production had been 1,200 units.

Units made and sold	1,000	1,200
	£	£
Variable costs:		
Direct materials	14,000	
Direct labour		
Fixed costs:		
Manufacturing overheads	45,000	
Total cost		
Cost per unit (to three decimal places)		

Task 9

(a)   The manager of Marginal Limited requires a performance report detailing budgeted data, actual data, and variances for last month.

Budgeted data for the month included:

Sales	8,350 units at £63 per unit
Material	14,150 kilos at £12 per kilo
Labour	14,130 hours at £19 per hour
Overheads	£189,500

In the table below, insert the budget amount for each item, calculate each variance, and then determine whether it is adverse or favourable.

Item	Budget £	Actual £	Variance £	Adverse / Favourable
Sales		524,000		
Material		149,960		
Labour		281,050		
Overheads		191,400		

(b)   A number of statements about budgeting are set out in the table below.

Identify whether the following statements are true or false.

	True	False
If budgeted sales are 7,000 units at £2.50 per unit, and actual sales value is £19,000, the sales variance is favourable		
If budgeted material costs are 9,000 units at £13.50 per unit, and actual material costs are £122,000, the material cost variance is favourable		
When variances are shown as percentages, the percentage is calculated based on the budget figures		
When a percentage variance is set to determine significant variances, only those variances below that percentage are reported		

Task 10

(a) The managers of Lovejoy Ltd require the budget report below for last month to be completed. In particular they want production cost variances expressed as percentages of budget.

Actual costs were:

Direct materials	£99,050
Direct labour	£80,560
Production overheads	£76,600

Calculate the production cost variances and the variances as a percentage of budget, rounded to two decimal places.

Cost	Budget £	Variance £	Variance %
Direct materials	96,350		
Direct labour	82,500		
Production overheads	71,090		

Sigma Ltd has a policy of identifying variances that exceed 4% of budget as significant, and then reporting only these variances to the appropriate manager(s).

(b) (i) Examine the variances in the following table and determine whether they are significant or not.

Cost	Budget £	Variance £	Significant
Direct materials	141,350	9,050	
Direct labour	189,500	10,160	
Production overheads	290,085	13,030	

(ii) Identify whether the following statements are true or false:

Statement	True	False
The direct material variance should be reported to the Purchasing Manager and Production Manager		
The direct labour variance should be reported to the Managing Director		
The direct labour variance should be reported to the Production Manager and Human Resources Manager		
The production overhead variance should be reported to the Production Manager		

Practice
assessment 3

Task 1

(a) **(1)** Identify **two** examples of terms used to classify cost **by nature** from the following list.

Term	
Direct	
Fixed	
Administration	
Indirect	
Labour	

(2) Complete the following sentences by using terms from the options:

(i) The cost of paying a factory manager would be considered **a direct / an indirect** cost.

(ii) The cost of paying a factory manager's basic salary would behave as a **fixed / variable / semi-variable** cost.

(b) The table below lists some of the characteristics of financial accounting and management accounting systems.

Indicate which characteristics relate to each system by putting a tick in the relevant column of the table below.

Characteristic	Financial Accounting	Management Accounting
One of its main outputs is a summarised historical financial statement that is produced annually		
One of its main purposes is useful information about costs within the organisation		
It can involve making comparisons between actual costs and budgeted costs		
Its output is controlled by legislation and accounting standards		

(c)   Zoom Ltd operates a garage business which comprises of second hand car sales and vehicle servicing. It uses an alpha-numeric coding structure based on one profit centre and three cost centres as outlined below. Each code has a sub-code so each transaction will be coded as */***

Profit/Cost Centre	Code	Sub-classification	Sub-code
Sales	W	Second Hand Car Sales	100
		Vehicle Servicing Sales	200
Second Hand Cars	X	Direct Cost	100
		Indirect Cost	200
Vehicle Servicing	Y	Direct Cost	100
		Indirect Cost	200
Administration	Z	Direct Cost	100
		Indirect Cost	200

Code the following revenue and cost transactions, which have been extracted from purchase invoices, sales invoices and payroll, using the table below.

Transaction	Code
Revenue from sale of Ford car to Mr Smith	
Cost of maintenance of electronic diagnostic equipment used for servicing vehicles	
Revenue from servicing vehicles during April	
Purchase cost of second hand cars at auction	
Cost of oil used to service vehicles	
Cost of wax used to polish cars ready for sale	

Task 2

(a)   Identify whether the following statements are true or false by putting a tick in the relevant column of the table below.

Statement	True	False
AVCO will always value issues based on last year's costs		
FIFO will value the inventory balance at the most recent prices		
LIFO will value the inventory balance at the most recent prices		

(b)   Identify one feature for each labour payment method by putting a tick in the relevant column of the table below.

Payment Method	Time-rate	Piecework	Time-rate plus bonus
All employees earn at least a certain amount, but efficient employees are rewarded with additional amounts			
Efficient employees will earn the same amount as inefficient employees			
An employee's pay would double if his output doubled			

(c)   Identify **two** of the following that are facts about using a budget:

A budget will show historical information	
A budget will always show exactly what will happen in the future	
A budget can help to plan for the future	
A sales budget will always have zero variances	
A budget can be used to monitor and control costs	

(d) Complete the following table to analyse the examples of various responsibility centres.

	Cost centre	Profit centre	Investment centre
An autonomous overseas division of a multi-national organisation			
An assembly section within a factory production department			
The electrical goods section within a department store			

Task 3

A company uses last in first out cost (LIFO) to value the issues and inventory of raw materials. The following record shows the raw material movements for the raw material P45 in December.

(a) Complete the inventory record. Costs per kilogram (kg) should be completed in £ to four decimal places.

Date	Receipts			Issues			Balance	
	Qty (kg)	Cost per kg	Total cost £	Qty (kg)	Cost per kg	Total cost £	Qty (kg)	Total cost £
1 Dec							20,000	50,000
6 Dec	15,000	2.65	39,750					
9 Dec				20,000				

(b) Complete the following table to show the value of the issue on 9 December and the inventory balance if the alternative valuation methods shown had been used.

Method	Valuation of Issue £	Closing inventory value £
FIFO		
AVCO		

Task 4

(a)   Nelson Ltd pays a time-rate of £9 per hour to its direct labour for a standard 38 hour week. Any of the labour force working in excess of 38 hours is paid an overtime rate of £13.50 per hour.

Calculate the gross wage for the week for the two workers in the table below.

Worker	Hours Worked	Basic Wage	Overtime	Gross Wage
M Singh	38	£	£	£
S Spencer	43	£	£	£

(b)   Nelson Ltd uses a time-rate method with bonus to pay its direct labour in one of its factories. The time-rate used is £8.50 per hour and a worker is expected to produce 4 units an hour. Anything over this and the worker is paid a bonus of £1.50 per unit.

Calculate the gross wage for the week including bonus for the three workers in the table below.

Worker	Hours Worked	Units Produced	Basic Wage	Bonus	Gross Wage
J Jarvis	40	150	£	£	£
S Poole	40	185	£	£	£
D Kerr	40	173	£	£	£

Task 5

Bedford Ltd is looking to calculate the unit cost of one of the products it makes. It needs to calculate an overhead absorption rate to apply to each unit. The methods it is considering are:

- Per machine hour
- Per labour hour
- Per unit

Total factory activity is forecast as follows:

Machine hours	90,000
Labour hours	235,000
Units	255,000
Overheads	£1,200,000

(a) Complete the table below to show the possible overhead absorption rates that Bedford Ltd could use. The absorption rates should be calculated to two decimal places.

	Machine hour	**Labour hour**	**Unit**
Overheads £			
Activity			
Absorption rate £			

The following data relates to the making of one unit of the product:

Material	9 kilos at £37.50 per kilo
Labour	1 hour at £23 per hour
Production time	30 minutes machine time

(b) Complete the table below (to two decimal places) to calculate the total unit cost, using the three overhead absorption rates you have calculated in (a).

Cost	**Machine hour £**	**Labour hour £**	**Unit £**
Material			
Labour			
Direct cost			
Overheads			
Total unit cost			

Task 6

(a) Identify the type of cost behaviour (fixed, variable, or semi-variable) described in each statement by ticking the relevant boxes in the table below.

Statement	Fixed	Variable	Semi-variable
At 900 units the cost is £25 per unit, and at 2,000 units the cost is £11.25 per unit			
At 7,500 units the cost is £61,875, and at 11,500 units the cost is £94,875			
At 3,800 units the cost is £15 per unit, and at 4,000 units the cost is £59,000			

(b) Complete the table below by inserting all costs for activity levels of 12,000 and 16,500 units.

	12,000 units	12,500 units	16,000 units	16,500 units
Variable cost £				
Fixed cost £				
Total cost £		288,400	351,400	

Task 7

A company has the following cost information for the last period:

	£
Raw materials used in production	117,000
Indirect raw materials	13,000
Direct labour	176,000
Indirect labour	15,000
Manufacturing expenses	98,000

Inventory information at the start and end of the period was as follows:

	£
Opening work in progress	37,000
Closing work in progress	49,000
Opening finished goods inventory	55,000
Closing finished goods inventory	38,000

Enter the correct figures for the following costs:

Cost structure for last period	£
Prime cost	
Manufacturing overheads	
Total manufacturing cost	
Cost of goods manufactured	
Cost of goods sold	

Task 8

A company uses weighted average cost (AVCO) to value the issues of raw materials to production. The following record shows the raw material movements for the raw material for product X50 in January.

(a) Complete the inventory record. Costs per kilogram (kg) should be completed in £ to four decimal places.

| Date | Receipts | | | Issues | | | Balance | |
	Qty (kg)	Cost per kg	Total cost £	Qty (kg)	Cost per kg	Total cost £	Qty (kg)	Total cost £
1 Jan							12,000	48,000
3 Jan	15,000	4.20	63,000					
5 Jan				18,000				

(b) Complete the following table to show:

- The costs for the actual January production of 36,000 units of X50, using the issues of raw materials calculated in part (a)
- The costs that would apply if the January production had been 42,000 units of X50

X50 Units made and sold	36,000	42,000
	£	£
Variable costs:		
Direct materials		
Direct labour	78,000	
Fixed costs:		
Manufacturing overheads	56,000	
Total cost		
Cost per unit (to three decimal places)		

Task 9

(a)   The manager of Deploy Limited requires a performance report detailing budgeted data, actual data, and variances for last month.

Budgeted data for the month included:

Sales	18,180 units at £64 per unit
Material	9,150 kilos at £17 per kilo
Labour	33,100 hours at £20 per hour
Overheads	£239,500

In the table below, insert the budget amount for each item, calculate each variance, and then determine whether it is adverse or favourable.

Item	Budget £	Actual £	Variance £	Adverse / Favourable
Sales		1,124,000		
Material		159,960		
Labour		695,080		
Overheads		241,400		

(b)   A number of statements about budgeting are set out in the table below.

Identify whether the following statements are true or false.

	True	False
If budgeted labour costs are 7,000 hours at £22.50 per hour, and actual labour costs are £160,500, the labour cost variance is favourable		
If budgeted material costs are 6,000 units at £19.50 per unit, and actual material costs are £116,900, the material cost variance is favourable		
Sales variances are favourable when the actual figure exceeds the budgeted figure		
When a percentage variance is set to determine significant variances, only those variances above that percentage are reported		

Task 10

(a)   The managers of McMillan Ltd require the budget report below for last month to be completed. In particular they want production cost variances expressed as percentages of budget.

Actual costs were:

Direct materials	£159,050
Direct labour	£130,560
Production overheads	£106,600

Calculate the production cost variances and the variances as a percentage of budget, rounded to two decimal places.

Cost	Budget £	Variance £	Variance %
Direct materials	161,350		
Direct labour	142,500		
Production overheads	111,000		

Omega Ltd has a policy of identifying variances that exceed 6% of budget as significant, and then reporting only these variances to the appropriate manager(s).

(b)   **(i)**   Examine the variances in the following table and determine whether they are significant or not.

Cost	Budget £	Variance £	Significant
Direct materials	201,050	9,050	
Direct labour	190,500	12,460	
Production overheads	220,000	17,050	

(ii)   Identify whether the following statements are true or false:

Statement	True	False
The direct material variance should be reported to the Purchasing Manager and Production Manager		
The direct labour variance should be reported to the Managing Director		
The direct labour variance should be reported to the Production Manager and Human Resources Manager		
The production overhead variance should be reported to the Training Manager		

Answers to practice assessment 1

Task 1

(a)   **(1)**

Term	
Materials	
Fixed	
Administration	✔
Indirect	
Production	✔

(2)   **(i)**   Costs that remain unchanged per unit of output are **variable** costs.

(ii)   Costs that remain unchanged in total are **fixed** costs.

(b)

Characteristic	Financial Accounting	Management Accounting
It is concerned with recording historic costs and revenues	✔	
One of its main purposes is to provide information for annual financial statements	✔	
It is accurate, with no use of estimates	✔	
It looks forward to show what is likely to happen in the future		✔

(c)

Transaction	Code
Factory lighting	B/200
Repairs to warehouse	D/200
Meat for making burgers	B/100
Sales to 'Kings Restaurant'	A/100
Commission to sales staff	D/200
Stationery for Administration	C/200

Task 2

(a)

	True	False
AVCO costs issues of inventory at the most recent purchase price		✔
FIFO costs issues of inventory at the oldest relevant purchase price	✔	
LIFO costs issues of inventory at the oldest relevant purchase price		✔
FIFO values closing inventory at the most recent purchase price	✔	
LIFO values closing inventory at the most recent purchase price		✔
AVCO values closing inventory at the most recent purchase price		✔

(b)

Payment Method	Time-rate	Piecework	Time-rate plus bonus
Labour is paid based entirely on attendance at the workplace	✔		
Labour is paid a basic rate plus an extra amount if an agreed level of production is exceeded			✔
Labour is paid entirely according to each individual's output		✔	

(c)

Showing historical information	
Monitoring against actual costs	✔
Planning for the future	✔
Calculating tax owed	
Calculating individuals' pay	

(d) **(1)** An individual shop within a chain of shops that is responsible for capital expenditure would be an example of **an investment** centre.

(2) A part of a business may be considered as a profit centre if it has responsibility for **income and costs**.

Task 3

Method	Value of Issue on 18 August	Inventory at 31 August
FIFO	£3,695	£2,505
LIFO	£3,760	£2,440
AVCO	£3,722	£2,478

Task 4

(a)

Worker	Hours Worked	Basic Wage	Overtime	Gross Wage
A Smith	37	£296.00	£0.00	£296.00
S Collins	41	£296.00	£64.00	£360.00

(b)

Worker	Hours Worked	Units Produced	Basic Wage	Bonus	Gross Wage
A Weaton	40	250	£400.00	£0.00	£400.00
J Davis	40	295	£400.00	£7.50	£407.50
M Laston	40	280	£400.00	£0.00	£400.00

Task 5

(a)

	Machine hour	Labour hour	Unit
Overheads £	450,000	450,000	450,000
Activity	35,000	60,000	80,000
Absorption rate £	12.86	7.50	5.63

(b)

Cost	Machine hour £	Labour hour £	Unit £
Material	30.00	30.00	30.00
Labour	9.00	9.00	9.00
Direct cost	39.00	39.00	39.00
Overheads	4.29	3.75	5.63
Total unit cost	43.29	42.75	44.63

Task 6

(a)

Costs	Fixed	Variable	Semi-variable
At 2,000 units the cost is £6,000, and at 9,000 units the cost is £27,000		✔	
At 1,500 units the cost is £2,500, and at 3,500 units the cost is £4,500			✔
At 1,200 units the cost is £6,000, and at 2,000 units the cost is £3 per unit	✔		

(b)

	2,000 units	3,000 units	5,000 units	6,500 units
Variable cost £	4,000			13,000
Fixed cost £	1,800			1,800
Total cost £	5,800	7,800	11,800	14,800

Task 7

Direct materials used	£47,000
Direct cost	£133,000
Manufacturing cost	£197,000
Cost of goods manufactured	£195,000
Cost of sales	£200,000

Task 8

(a)

Date	Receipts			Issues			Balance	
	Qty (kg)	Cost per kg	Total cost £	Qty (kg)	Cost per kg	Total cost £	Qty (kg)	Total cost £
1 Nov							10,000	50,000
6 Nov	15,000	5.20	78,000				25,000	128,000
9 Nov				20,000	5.120	102,400	5,000	25,600

(b)

Z15 Units made and sold	10,000	8,000
	£	£
Variable costs:		
Direct materials	102,400	81,920
Direct labour	50,000	40,000
Fixed costs:		
Manufacturing overheads	25,000	25,000
Total cost	177,400	146,920
Cost per unit (to three decimal places)	17.740	18.365

Task 9

(a)

Item	Budget £	Actual £	Variance £	Adverse / Favourable
Sales	283,500	284,000	500	Favourable
Material	48,750	49,560	810	Adverse
Labour	73,700	71,600	2,100	Favourable
Overheads	99,500	95,900	3,600	Favourable

(b)

	True	False
If budgeted sales are 8,000 units at £2.50 per unit, and actual sales value is £22,000, the sales variance is favourable	✔	
If budgeted material costs are 2,000 units at £11.50 per unit, and actual material costs are £22,000, the material cost variance is favourable	✔	
When variances are shown as percentages, the percentage is calculated based on the actual figures		✔
The total value of all favourable variances can never exceed the total value of all adverse variances		✔

Task 10

(a)

Cost	Budget £	Variance £	Variance %
Direct materials	71,350	2,400	3.36
Direct labour	88,500	1,060	1.20
Production overheads	44,050	550	1.25

(b)　(1)

Cost	Budget £	Variance £	Significant
Direct materials	96,350	4,050	✔
Direct labour	109,500	3,160	
Production overheads	77,055	2,030	

(2)

Statement	True	False
The direct material variance should be reported to the Purchasing Manager and Production Manager	✔	
The direct labour variance should be reported to the Managing Director		✔
The production overhead variance should be reported to the Training Manager		✔
The production overhead variance should be reported to the Production Manager		✔

Answers to practice assessment 2

Task 1

(a) (1)

Term	
Materials	✔
Fixed	
Administration	
Indirect	
Labour	✔

(2) (i) Cost of renting factory premises would behave as a **fixed** cost.

(ii) Cost of paying production workers on a piecework basis would behave as a **variable** cost.

(b)

Characteristic	Financial Accounting	Management Accounting
The system is subject to many external regulations	✔	
The accounts must be produced in a format that is imposed on the organisation	✔	
The system is governed primarily by its usefulness to its internal users		✔
The information produced can be in any format that the organisation wishes to use		✔

(c)

Transaction	Code
Revenue from project in Saudi Arabia	PR200
Cost of material used for project in Saudi Arabia	PC030
Cost of hiring local labour for project in Saudi Arabia	PC040
Investment in project in Saudi Arabia	IP200
Revenue from UK project	PR100
Cost of renting project offices	PC050

Task 2

(a)

Statement	True	False
AVCO uses a weighted average to value both issues and balances	✔	
FIFO will value issues at the most recent prices		✔
LIFO will value issues at the most recent prices	✔	

(b)

Statement	True	False
If during a 40 hour week the employee produces 300 units a bonus of £50 will apply	✔	
If during a 37 hour week the employee produces 250 units no bonus will apply	✔	
If during a 39 hour week the employee produces 320 units a bonus of £67.50 will apply		✔

(c)

Showing historical information	✔
Monitoring against actual costs	
Planning for the future	
Coordinating planning activities	
Recording petty cash	✔

(d)   **(1)**   Where an organisation produces many different products with different values it **should not** use a per unit overhead absorption method.

(2)   For a labour-intensive manufacturing organisation, the most appropriate overhead absorption method would be **direct labour hours**.

Task 3

Method	Cost of Issue on 18 February	Value of Inventory at 28 February
FIFO	£3,420	£3,030
LIFO	£3,480	£2,970
AVCO	£3,440	£3,010

Task 4

	Hours	Cost £
Basic hours and pay	1,400	14,000
Unsocial hours premium		1,400
Overtime hours basic rate	200	2,000
Overtime hours premium		500
Bonus payment		1,600
Total pay		19,500

Task 5

(a)

	Machine hour	Labour hour	Unit
Overheads £	380,000	380,000	380,000
Activity	20,000	35,000	75,000
Absorption rate £	19.00	10.86	5.07

(b)

Cost	Machine hour £	Labour hour £	Unit £
Material	30.00	30.00	30.00
Labour	4.00	4.00	4.00
Direct cost	34.00	34.00	34.00
Overheads	3.17	2.72	5.07
Total unit cost	37.17	36.72	39.07

Task 6

(a)

Costs	Fixed	Variable	Semi-variable
At 3,000 units the cost is £16,000, and at 6,000 units the cost is £27,000			✔
At 2,500 units the cost is £7,500, and at 7,500 units the cost is £22,500		✔	
At 1,800 units the cost is £5 per unit, and at 2,000 units the cost is £4.50 per unit	✔		

(b)

	5,000 units	6,000 units	10,000 units	10,500 units
Variable cost £	17,500			36,750
Fixed cost £	1,500			1,500
Total cost £	19,000	22,500	36,500	38,250

Task 7

Direct materials used	£109,000
Direct cost	£265,000
Manufacturing cost	£411,000
Cost of goods manufactured	£399,000
Cost of goods sold	£401,000

Task 8

(a)

	Cost per Production Worker £	Total Cost £
Basic pay	2,250	56,250
Attendance premium	45	1,125
Bonus payment	20	500
Total pay	2,315	57,875

(b)

Units made and sold	1,000	1,200
	£	£
Variable costs:		
Direct materials	14,000	16,800
Direct labour	57,875	69,450
Fixed costs:		
Manufacturing overheads	45,000	45,000
Total cost	116,875	131,250
Cost per unit (to three decimal places)	116.875	109.375

Task 9

(a)

Item	Budget £	Actual £	Variance £	Adverse / Favourable
Sales	526,050	524,000	2,050	Adverse
Material	169,800	149,960	19,840	Favourable
Labour	268,470	281,050	12,580	Adverse
Overheads	189,500	191,400	1,900	Adverse

(b)

	True	False
If budgeted sales are 7,000 units at £2.50 per unit, and actual sales value is £19,000, the sales variance is favourable	✔	
If budgeted material costs are 9,000 units at £13.50 per unit, and actual material costs are £122,000, the material cost variance is favourable		✔
When variances are shown as percentages, the percentage is calculated based on the budget figures	✔	
When a percentage variance is set to determine significant variances, only those variances below that percentage are reported		✔

Task 10

(a)

Cost	Budget £	Variance £	Variance %
Direct materials	96,350	2,700	2.80
Direct labour	82,500	1,940	2.35
Production overheads	71,090	5,510	7.75

(b)   (i)

Cost	Budget £	Variance £	Significant
Direct materials	141,350	9,050	✔
Direct labour	189,500	10,160	✔
Production overheads	290,085	13,030	✔

(ii)

Statement	True	False
The direct material variance should be reported to the Purchasing Manager and Production Manager	✔	
The direct labour variance should be reported to the Managing Director		✔
The direct labour variance should be reported to the Production Manager and Human Resources Manager	✔	
The production overhead variance should be reported to the Production Manager	✔	

Answers to practice assessment 3

Task 1

(a) **(1)**

Term	
Direct	✔
Fixed	
Administration	
Indirect	✔
Labour	

(2) **(i)** The cost of paying a factory manager would be considered **an indirect** cost.

(ii) The cost of paying a factory manager's basic salary would behave as a **fixed** cost.

(b)

Characteristic	Financial Accounting	Management Accounting
One of its main outputs is a summarised historical financial statement that is produced annually	✔	
One of its main purposes is useful information about costs within the organisation		✔
It can involve making comparisons between actual costs and budgeted costs		✔
Its output is controlled by legislation and accounting standards	✔	

(c)

Transaction	Code
Revenue from sale of Ford car to Mr Smith	W/100
Cost of maintenance of electronic diagnostic equipment used for servicing vehicles	Y/200
Revenue from servicing vehicles during April	W/200
Purchase cost of second hand cars at auction	X/100
Cost of oil used to service vehicles	Y/100
Cost of wax used to polish cars ready for sale	X/200

Task 2

(a)

Statement	True	False
AVCO will always value issues based on last year's costs		✔
FIFO will value the inventory balance at the most recent prices	✔	
LIFO will value the inventory balance at the most recent prices		✔

(b)

Payment Method	Time-rate	Piecework	Time-rate plus bonus
All employees earn at least a certain amount, but efficient employees are rewarded with additional amounts			✔
Efficient employees will earn the same amount as inefficient employees	✔		
An employee's pay would double if his output doubled		✔	

(c)

A budget will show historical information	
A budget will always show exactly what will happen in the future	
A budget can help to plan for the future	✔
A sales budget will always have zero variances	
A budget can be used to monitor and control costs	✔

(d)

	Cost centre	Profit centre	Investment centre
An autonomous overseas division of a multi-national organisation			✔
An assembly section within a factory production department	✔		
The electrical goods section within a department store		✔	

Task 3

(a)

Date	Receipts			Issues			Balance	
	Qty (kg)	Cost per kg	Total cost £	Qty (kg)	Cost per kg	Total cost £	Qty (kg)	Total cost £
1 Dec							20,000	50,000
6 Dec	15,000	2.65	39,750				35,000	89,750
9 Dec				20,000	2.6125	52,250	15,000	37,500

(b)

Method	Valuation of Issue £	Closing inventory value £
FIFO	50,000	39,750
AVCO	51,286	38,464

Task 4

(a)

Worker	Hours Worked	Basic Wage	Overtime	Gross Wage
M Singh	38	£342.00	£0.00	£342.00
S Spencer	43	£342.00	£67.50	£409.50

(b)

Worker	Hours Worked	Units Produced	Basic Wage	Bonus	Gross Wage
J Jarvis	40	150	£340.00	£0.00	£340.00
S Poole	40	185	£340.00	£37.50	£377.50
D Kerr	40	173	£340.00	£19.50	£359.50

Task 5

(a)

	Machine hour	Labour hour	Unit
Overheads £	1,200,000	1,200,000	1,200,000
Activity	90,000	235,000	255,000
Absorption rate £	13.33	5.11	4.71

(b)

Cost	Machine hour £	Labour hour £	Unit £
Material	337.50	337.50	337.50
Labour	23.00	23.00	23.00
Direct cost	360.50	360.50	360.50
Overheads	6.67	5.11	4.71
Total unit cost	367.17	365.61	365.21

Task 6

(a)

Statement	Fixed	Variable	Semi-variable
At 900 units the cost is £25 per unit and at 2,000 units the cost is £11.25 per unit	✔		
At 7,500 units the cost is £61,875, and at 11,500 units the cost is £94,875		✔	
At 3,800 units the cost is £15 per unit, and at 4,000 units the cost is £59,000			✔

(b)

	12,000 units	12,500 units	16,000 units	16,500 units
Variable cost £	216,000			297,000
Fixed cost £	63,400			63,400
Total cost £	279,400	288,400	351,400	360,400

Task 7

Cost structure for last period	£
Prime cost	293,000
Manufacturing overheads	126,000
Total manufacturing cost	419,000
Cost of goods manufactured	407,000
Cost of goods sold	424,000

Task 8

(a)

Date	Receipts Qty (kg)	Cost per kg	Total cost £	Issues Qty (kg)	Cost per kg	Total cost £	Balance Qty (kg)	Total cost £
1 Jan							12,000	48,000
3 Jan	15,000	4.20	63,000				27,000	111,000
5 Jan				18,000	4.1111	74,000	9,000	37,000

(b)

X50 Units made and sold	36,000	42,000
	£	£
Variable costs:		
Direct materials	74,000	86,333
Direct labour	78,000	91,000
Fixed costs:		
Manufacturing overheads	56,000	56,000
Total cost	208,000	233,333
Cost per unit (to 3 decimal places)	5.778	5.556

Task 9

(a)

Item	Budget £	Actual £	Variance £	Adverse / Favourable
Sales	1,163,520	1,124,000	39,520	Adverse
Material	155,550	159,960	4,410	Adverse
Labour	662,000	695,080	33,080	Adverse
Overheads	239,500	241,400	1,900	Adverse

(b)

	True	False
If budgeted labour costs are 7,000 hours at £22.50 per hour, and actual labour costs are £160,500, the labour cost variance is favourable		✔
If budgeted material costs are 6,000 units at £19.50 per unit, and actual material costs are £116,900, the material cost variance is favourable	✔	
Sales variances are favourable when the actual figure exceeds the budgeted figure	✔	
When a percentage variance is set to determine significant variances, only those variances above that percentage are reported	✔	

Task 10

(a)

Cost	Budget £	Variance £	Variance %
Direct materials	161,350	2,300	1.43
Direct labour	142,500	11,940	8.38
Production overheads	111,000	4,400	3.96

(b) **(i)**

Cost	Budget £	Variance £	Significant
Direct materials	201,050	9,050	
Direct labour	190,500	12,460	✔
Production overheads	220,000	17,050	✔

(ii)

Statement	True	False
The direct material variance should be reported to the Purchasing Manager and Production Manager		✔
The direct labour variance should be reported to the Managing Director		✔
The direct labour variance should be reported to the Production Manager and Human Resources Manager	✔	
The production overhead variance should be reported to the Training Manager		✔

for your notes

for your notes

for your notes

for your notes

for your notes

for your notes

for your notes

for your notes

for your notes

for your notes

for your notes

for your notes